FIREMAN SAM
ON THE
MOVE

Illustrated by The County Studio

HEINEMANN • LONDON

William Heinemann Ltd, Michelin House,
81 Fulham Road, London SW3 6RB

LONDON MELBOURNE AUCKLAND

First published 1992 by William Heinemann Ltd
Fireman Sam copyright © 1985 Prism Art & Design Ltd
Text copyright © 1992 William Heinemann Ltd
Illustrations copyright © 1992 William Heinemann Ltd
All rights reserved
Based on the animation series produced by
Bumper Films for S4C – Channel 4 Wales –
and Prism Art & Design Ltd
Original idea by Dave Gingell and Dave Jones,
assisted by Mike Young
Characters created by Rob Lee

ISBN 434 96018 7

Produced by Mandarin Offset
Printed and bound in Hong Kong

Fireman Sam drives through Pontypandy in Jupiter the fire engine.

How many wheels has Jupiter got?

First, he stops at Dilys Price's shop for a newspaper.

What colour is Jupiter?

"Look, Fireman Sam!" says Norman. "It's my robot!"

What colour is Norman's robot?

Dilys shows Fireman Sam her new shopping trolley.

How many wheels has the trolley got?

Then, he meets James outside on his scooter.

Where is James going on his scooter?

Elvis zooms past on his motorbike.
He's on holiday today.

What colour is Elvis's helmet?

Sarah comes to find James on her bicycle.

Which goes faster, Elvis's motorbike or Sarah's bicycle?

As Fireman Sam drives out of Pontypandy,
a truck drives past Jupiter.

What do you think is inside the truck?

Then he sees Trevor on his way back from Newtown.

Where is Trevor's bus going?

Fireman Sam has to wait at the roadworks.
He watches the digger make a hole.

What colours are the traffic lights?

Then the crane lowers a pipe into the hole.

Which vehicle has round wheels, the digger or the crane?

When Fireman Sam arrives at the fire station,
Penny Morris is waiting by Venus, her rescue tender.

How many buttons has Penny's jacket got?

Penny sees the farmer driving his tractor across the fields towards them.

What colour is the tractor?

There has been an accident at the roadworks.
"Let's get down there quickly!" says Fireman Sam.

Where are the large wheels on the tractor?

Fireman Sam and Penny Morris race down the hill in their fire engines.

Which fire engine is in front?

A dumper truck has fallen into a hole.

What is Penny carrying?

Fireman Sam and Penny fasten the ropes, then Jupiter pulls the dumper truck out of the hole.

Is Jupiter moving backwards or forwards?

"Nice work, Sam," says Penny when the truck is safely out of the hole.

How many wheels has the dumper truck got?

Then the dumper truck is towed away to be mended.

How many wheels can you see in the picture?

Fireman Sam and Penny go back to the fire station.

Which fire engine has six wheels?

"Well done," says Station Officer Steele when they tell him about the accident.

What colour is Station Officer Steele's car?

Fireman Sam and Penny go to Pontypandy.
Norman on his skateboard almost knocks them over!

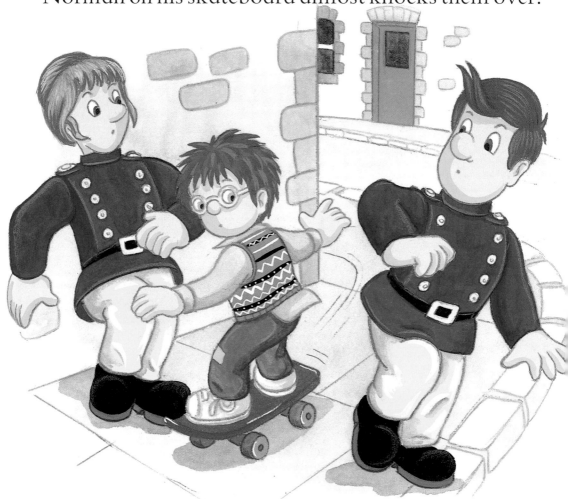

What colour is Norman's skateboard?

"I've finished Bella's gardening, so I'm going to the park," says Trevor. "Why don't you come?"

How many wheels has Trevor's wheelbarrow got?

Fireman Sam buys everyone an ice-cream.
James and Sarah have theirs first.

What colour is Bella's ice-cream stall?

Then they decide to go roller skating, and Penny joins in!

How many roller skates can you see?